Quercus

by Ian Freemantle

A story for children

Introduction

Quercus is in the style of an old English fable which aims to explain the ever changing seasons. The main character 'Quercus', represented by a tree spirit, undergoes a reluctant change when visited by other tree spirits: Sage, Solstice, Autumnal and Yule.

He finally sits around the camp fire with the last visitor and looks back with fondness on the passing year before the whole cycle of life begins again.

BEST WISHES,

Quercus

First published in December 2019 by Black Pear Press
www.blackpear.net

Copyright © Ian Freemantle 2019

ISBN 978-1-913418-09-0

Foreground illustrations by Richard Frost
Background oak leaf motifs by Tony Judge

Black Pear Press

The History of Quercus

In 1467 an acorn leapt unto fate, bound for the soils of Albion, against the wishes of medieval herd and bread-maker, it put down its claim for this space. Four centuries and five score years it formed its Quercus robur, exhibiting its mighty torso for the valley below. Witness to failings of landscape directors, it outlived them all. "Eternal," they chanted! "Touch wood for good fortune," they wished! Dependable limb outstretched for balance, grabbing at elements, leapt unto fate to join the wretched soils of war torn meadow.

Now: perch for wren, scratch post for sheep, the bugs, worms and mites sculpted away, taking their time to ensure the perfect finish. To complete, they summoned a passing woodcutter to take on their vision. He lay out the pieces for weeks, placing them this way and that. Finally, under the harvest sun in Albion he took up his tools of haste to release the spirit of oak for all to see. This half-millennia fellow born of the soil of Albion may outlive us all.

"Eternal," they chanted! "Touch wood for good fortune," they wished!

Quercus is an ancient fellow
who doesn't fancy change,
he often feels quite nervous
when nature's rearranged.

There's movement in the meadow,
there's stirring in the grass,
Jack Frost gives way to sunshine
and the snow is melting fast.

Buds burst on the early Ash,
that's how they get their name.
"Oh humbug," mutters Quercus,
"I wish things would stay the same."

"I'll have to find new leaves again
and push out some new shoots,
I get so very nervous when Sage
puts on her spring time boots."

Sage is a sprightly soul
of a certain ilk,
she gathers up the morning dew,
turns cobwebs into silk.

She's best friends with the fairies,
the buzzards and the bees,
her early rays warm the earth to
wake up all the trees.

But not old Quercus, oh no!
Quercus is an ancient fellow
who doesn't fancy change,
he often feels quite nervous
when nature's rearranged.

The sun is high up in the sky,
the days are drawing long,
the daisies dance the meadow
and the blackbird's in full song.

The race to get full leaves this year
was won again by oak.
"Oh humbug," mutters Quercus,
"now we're bound to get a soak!"

"I'll have to hold my limbs up high,
supporting tons of leaves,
and make some extra acorns
to allow for all the thieves."

Now Solstice joins the seasons,
he's elegant and bold,
he holds the sun high in the sky
to keep away the cold.

But he's gentle with old Quercus
and rocks him in the breeze,
this helps him spread his pollen
and makes everybody SNEEZE!!!!

But not old Quercus, oh no!
Quercus is an ancient fellow
who doesn't fancy change,
he often feels quite nervous
when nature's rearranged.

But even humbug Quercus
has to admit and admire,
he knows he simply looks his best
when his leaves turn crimson fire.

Skipping through the hedgerow
with a paintbrush in her hand,
Autumunal spreads her magic
all across the land.

"Oh humbug," mutters Quercus,
"the morning sky is red,
I hope that all those Shepherds
are tucked up in their beds."

Whilst Autumunal paints her magic,
she sings her soulful tune
and helps nature's harvest gather
under the scarlet moon.

But the light is fading quickly
and the autumn breeze is cool,
Quercus knows Autumunal
brings the greatest change of all.

You see Quercus is an ancient fellow
and for change he does not care,
especially when the winter frost
lays the woodland trees all bare.

Ho ho! Sounds of chopping firewood,
bound for winter fuel,
chestnuts roasting on a fire,
must mean his good friend Yule.

Yule is quite traditional
and full of festive cheer,
Quercus enjoys his company
at this time every year.

They sit around the fire
until the morning mist
and talk about the year gone by
and start to reminisce.

"Oh humbug," mutters Quercus,
"I miss the cuckoo's song,
the evening sky is empty now
the swallows have all gone."

"I miss the crimson sunrise,
I miss the soft spring breeze,
I miss Solstice's sunshine
making everybody SNEEZE!!!"

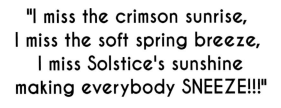

"I miss Autumunal's magic
and the colour that she brings,
I miss the daisies dancing
and the blackbird when she sings."

The weather's always changing
and the seasons never last,
there's movement in the meadow
and the snow is melting fast.

Quercus is an ancient fellow
who doesn't fancy change,
he often feels quite nervous
when nature's rearranged.